robbie williams

I've been expecting you

Exclusive Distributors
International Music Publications Limited
Griffin House, 161 Hammersmith Road, London W6 8BS, England

International Music Publications GmbH, Germany
Marstallstraße 8, D-80539 Munchen, Germany

Nuova Carish S.p.A.
Via Campania, 12 20098 S. Giuliano Milanese (MI)
Zona Industriale Sesto Ulteriano, Italy
20, rue de la Ville-l'Eveque-75008 Paris, France

Danmusik
Vognmagergade 7, DK-1120 Copenhagen K, Denmark

Warner/Chappell Music Australia Pty Ltd.
3 Talavera Road, North Ryde, New South Wales 2113, Australia

Folio © 1999 International Music Publications Ltd
Griffin House, 161 Hammersmith Road, London W6 8BS, England

Printed by The Panda Group · Haverhill · Suffolk CB9 8PR · UK
Binding by Suffolk Bound · Ipswich

Photograph: Hamish Brown

robbie williams

There was a moment recently when Robbie Williams graduated from being merely an infamous former teen star with a successful solo album and a brace of hit singles under his belt into a genuine, bona fide pop icon. You can pin-point the actual instant the nation took him conclusively to their hearts because it happened at this year's Glastonbury festival in front of the biggest Pyramid stage crowd ever assembled. And as Robbie launched into *'Let Me Entertain You'* he managed to unite the most disparate of audiences with one rather old fashioned conceit: classic pop showmanship. It was here (ironically at this very site in 1995 that marked both the symbolic end to his tumultuous tenure with Take That and the kick-start to his solo career) that Robbie proved himself to be this country's supreme pop performer. Finally, publicly, Robbie had managed to lay to rest his turbulent rollercoaster past. Take That, booze, drugs, rehab, celebrity shags and a catalogue of lurid tabloid headlines - Robbie made all this irrelevant by displaying a deeper understanding of the pure adrenaline rush that only the most brilliant pop music can produce more than any of his contemporaries could ever dare - of course, Robbie says that he's known all along that he had it in himself to be a world class performer. It just took a while for the rest of us to catch up. "I'm an old - fashioned entertainer," he says. "There's nobody else around like me. And I'm serious when I say let me entertain you - I'm not joking - let me do it - and I guarantee you'll have a fantastic time."

Of course, it could all have been so different. After all, you can count on the fingers of one hand the number of teen pop stars who have successfully re-invented themselves as major league, mainstream performers. It would have been all too easy after Take That's messy demise for Robbie to turn into this generation's Andrew Ridgeley. And for a while it looked like he might.

"In the past I've made it hard for people to take me and my music seriously," Robbie admits. "I'd been cocooned for so long that when I was finally released I didn't have a clue what I was doing. I was very young and very stupid and it was inevitable that I was going to fall on the wrong side of the tracks." "There had been hints all along of course that Robbie would end up on top. He was always the most interesting one in Take That, and *'Freedom'*, his post Take That single had sold more than a quarter of a million copies. More than a year later his debut solo album, *'Life Thru a Lens'* (released in September '97) became the sleeper hit of the year. Overcoming its slow start (it didn't actually reach No.1 until its 28th week of release!) it is rapidly approaching sixtuple platinum status and continues to sell strongly. The turning point was *'Angels'*, the single that tipped the album from respectable into stratospheric sales. "Last year I'd had two number two singles, a top 10 and a top 20," Robbie recalls. "The album had sold about 33,000 copies - which is bugger all as far as I'm concerned. Then *'Angels'* comes out and suddenly the album goes from 33,000 to 300,000 sales. Then two weeks later it went double platinum. I was a very happy boy! An ecstatically received, sell-out British tour confirmed Robbie's burgeoning popularity. The icing on the cake was the massive success of the album's last single, and Robbie's theme song, *'Let Me Entertain You'*. Cue mass adulation, critical acclaim, awards and immense record sales.

All he had to do next was do it all again.

So he has. Written with full-time collaborator Guy Chambers over the last twelve months in the back of tour buses and in dressing rooms all over the world, *'I've Been Expecting You'* is Robbie's not-so-difficult second album. Rather than make another *'Life Thru a Lens'* he's crafted the kind of all too rare gem of an album that will have journalists scrabbling for their thesauruses. Expect words like breathtaking, stirring, exuberant, classic and genre-bending to be bandied around with considerable abandon once the album hits the shelves on 26th October 1998. *'I've Been Expecting You'* is not only the most anticipated album of 1998, it's also the best. Reflecting both Robbie's wildly eclectic musical tastes and every facet of his personality, the album's knockout tracks are indelible proof of Robbie's versatility and sparkling songwriting talent. *'I've Been Expecting You'* is the sound of a more confident, focused Robbie ("Basically it's just like Life Thru a Lens but with a better standard of songs," he says self-depreciatingly. "I'm not being disrespectful to the last album but this one is better.") You may already know that the album contains the awesome first single *'Millennium'*. Based around a legendary sample from John Barry's Bond theme from 'You Only Live Twice', it's one of the most infectious songs Robbie has ever written.

"The album's most enjoyable song to write was *'Millennium'*," Robbie says. "The John Barry sample is my favourite strings part ever. We connected it to a hip-hop beat. And the lyrics just came instantaneously. It's about how in the greater scheme of things we're all quite irrelevant. And I kept thinking how all this talk of the Millennium brought it into focus. The line "We all enjoy the madness because we're all gonna fade away" is me saying "go on - go out and get off your head!"

'I've Been Expecting You' also houses the much-mooted collaboration between Robbie and two of his musical heroes, Neil Tennant of the Pet Shop Boys and the Divine Comedy's Neil Hannon. The result, *'No Regrets'*, is simply brilliant.

From the guitar heavy rock and roller *'Karma Killer'* to the whimsical, surprisingly heart felt, *'Heaven From Here'*, *'I've Been Expecting You'* is an absolute breath of fresh air in an increasingly stale music scene. The album also confirms Robbie's burgeoning reputation as a potent lyricist with a canny style, reminiscent of Rod Stewart at his Faces-era best. "When I sat down to write this album the lyrics came out in a whoosh," Robbie explains. "it was like an explosion. And it still is. It's coming out all over the place. I didn't really plan how I wanted it to sound. Guy and I said, "Let's just sit down and see where this takes us. "When we started writing I just thought, "We've got it right then. Great!" And we went from there."

Unsurprisingly, Robbie must have the last word. "My head is in a much better place than when I released my first album," he says. "Perhaps I've got delusions of grandeur but I genuinely believe that this is going to be the most important pop album of the year."

STRONG

Words and Music by
Robert Williams and Guy Chambers

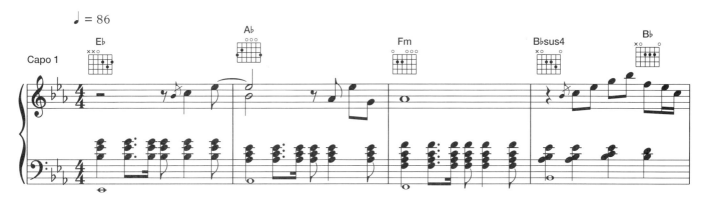

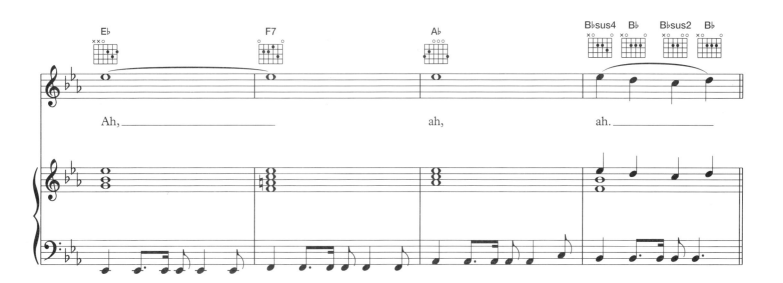

Ah,_____ ah, ah._____

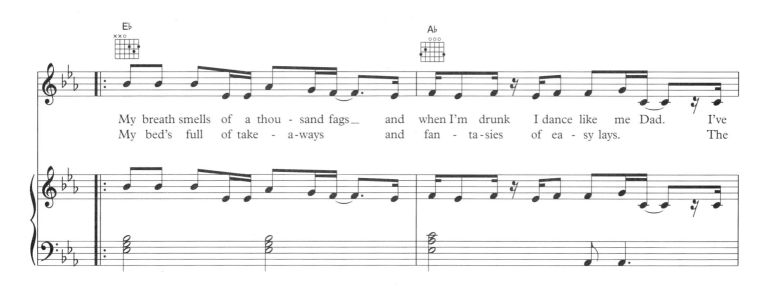

My breath smells of a thou-sand fags__ and when I'm drunk I dance like me Dad. I've
My bed's full of take - a - ways and fan - ta - sies of ea - sy lays. The

NO REGRETS

Words and Music by
Robert Williams and Guy Chambers

I know from the out - side   we look good for each oth - er.

Felt things were go - ing   wrong when   you did-n't like my moth - er.

MILLENNIUM

Words and Music by
Robert Williams, Guy Chambers
John Barry and Leslie Bricusse

PHOENIX FROM THE FLAMES

Words and Music by
Robert Williams and Guy Chambers

WIN SOME LOSE SOME

Words and Music by
Robert Williams and Guy Chambers

Ooh._____

I did - n't know what we had found, just caught the bus and rode___ it to town.

She would - n't no - tice an - y-thing else but me._____

Your

GRACE

Words and Music by
Robert Williams and Guy Chambers

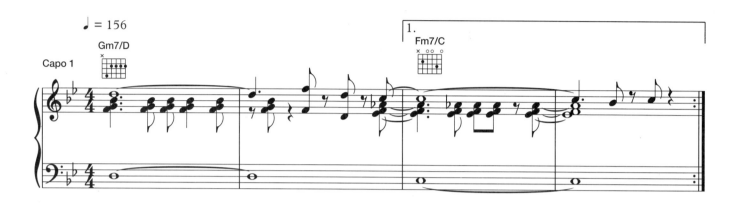

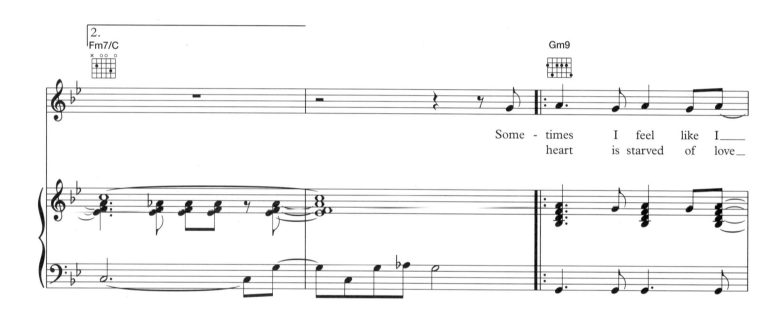

Some - times I feel like I____ am sail - ing on a sunk - en dream.

heart is starved of love____ in these ra - di - o days.____ I

38

JESUS IN A CAMPER VAN

Words and Music by
Robert Williams, Guy Chambers and Woody Guthrie

Oo, ah.___ Oo, ah.___

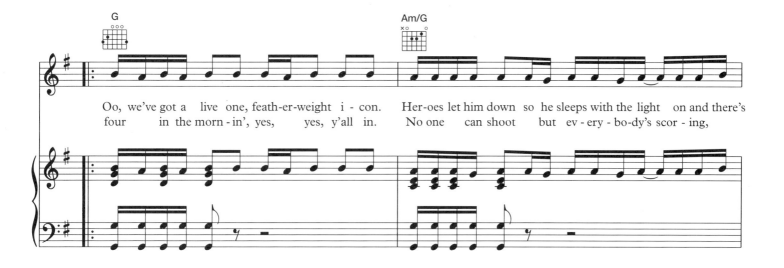

Oo, we've got a live one, feath-er-weight i - con. Her-oes let him down so he sleeps with the light on and there's

four in the morn - in', yes, yes, y'all in. No one can shoot but ev - ery - bo-dy's scor - ing,

noth-ing left to do. Kneel down and pray.___

trust me it's bor - ing. Get down and pray.

They

HEAVEN FROM HERE

Words and Music by
Robert Williams and Guy Chambers

KARMA KILLER

Words and Music by
Robert Williams and Guy Chambers

SHE'S THE ONE

Words and Music by
Karl Wallinger

MAN MACHINE

Words and Music by
Robert Williams and Guy Chambers

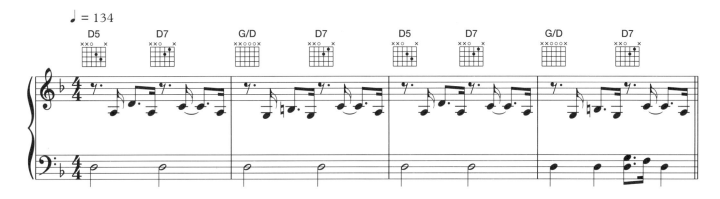

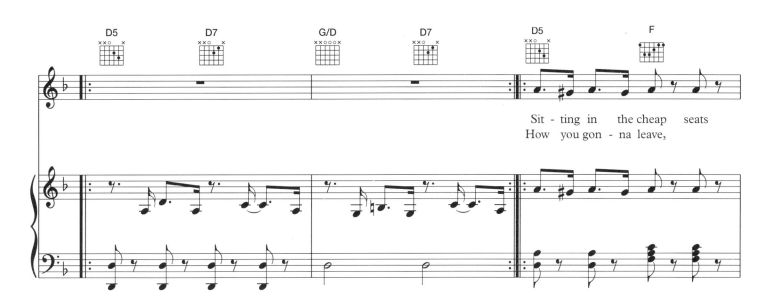

Sit - ting in the cheap seats
How you gon - na leave,

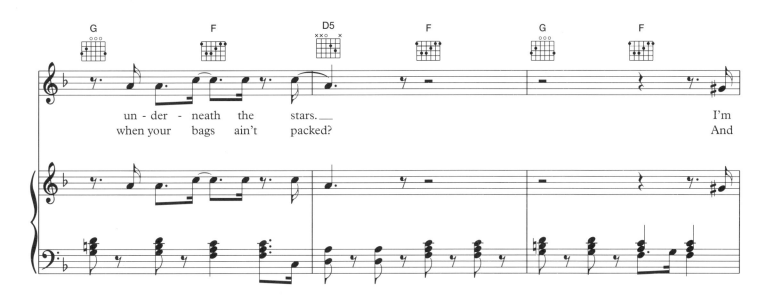

un - der - neath the stars.___ I'm
when your bags ain't packed? And

THESE DREAMS

Words and Music by
Robert Williams and Guy Chambers

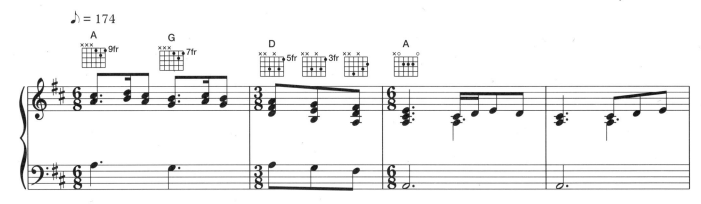

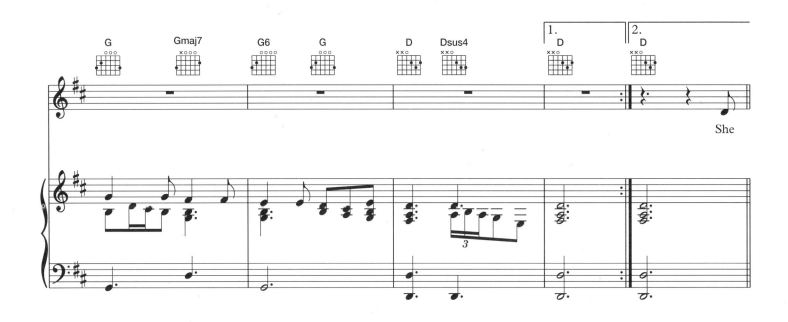

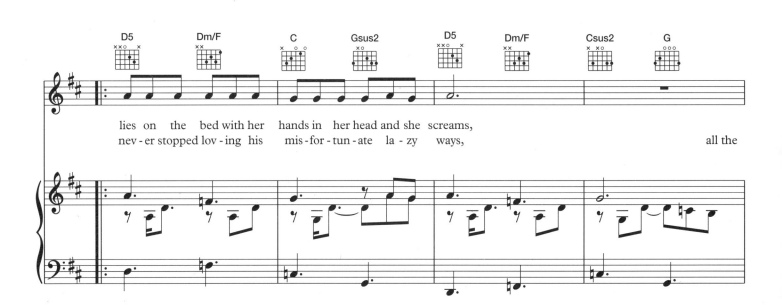

STAND YOUR GROUND

Words and Music by
Robert Williams and Guy Chambers

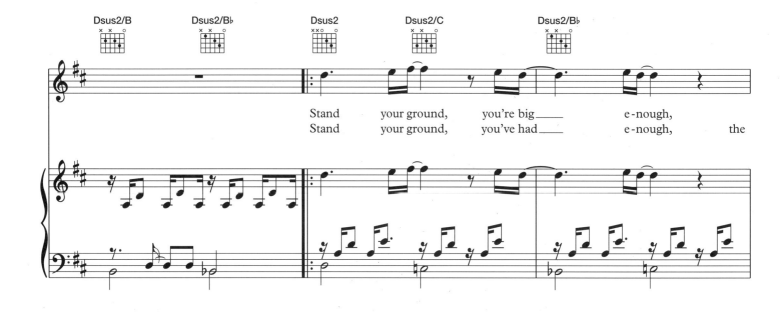

Stand your ground, you're big_____ e-nough,
Stand your ground, you've had_____ e-nough, the

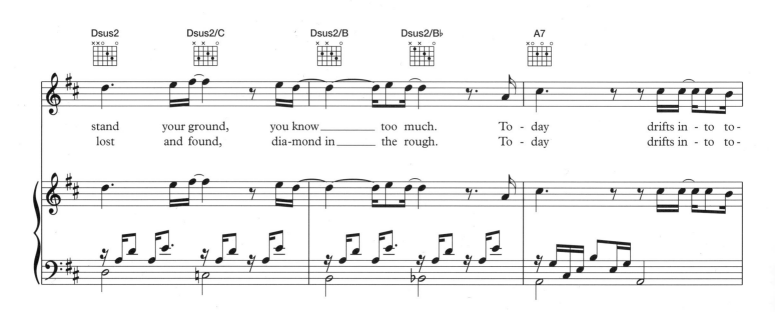

stand your ground, you know_____ too much. To-day drifts in-to to-
lost and found, dia-mond in_____ the rough. To-day drifts in-to to-

- mor-row,_____ and you can al - most taste the sor - row.
- mor-row,_____ you feel_____ your soul's been bor - rowed.

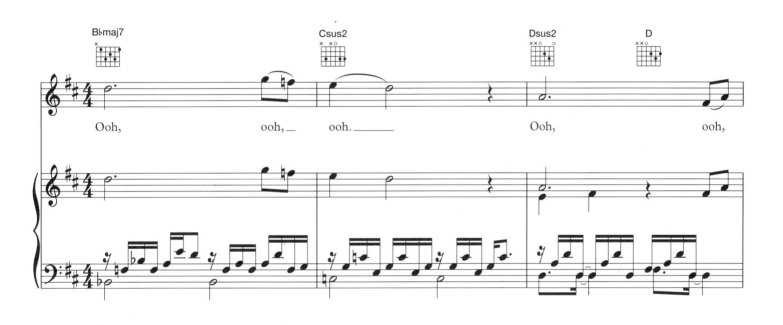

Ooh, ooh,__ ooh._____ Ooh, ooh,

ooh. Ooh, ooh,__ ooh._____

STALKERS DAY OFF

Words and Music by
Robert Williams, Guy Chambers and Fil Eisler

Printed in England
The Panda Group · Haverhill · Suffolk · 1/99